DAILY FOOD FOR THOUGHT

JANUARY

_____

YEAR

_____

NAME

BECAUSE AN UNEXAMINED LIFE
IS NOT WORTH LIVING —SOCRATES

Other books by Timber Hawkeye:

Buddhist Boot Camp is a collection of eight years' worth of journal entries and letters to friends, which is why each chapter is only a page long and can be read in any order.

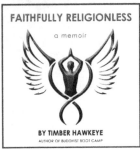

Faithfully Religionless is about discovering the difference between feelings and emotions, the disparity between truths and facts, and the countless benefits of mindful living.

Hawkeye Publishers

Manao: January

For more information, address Hawkeye Publishers
HAWKEYEPUBLISHERS.COM

ISBN: 978-1946005502

Why we journal...

I often invite people to list their core values and write down their vision statement. Once it's on paper, we can cross reference what we've written with the life we are actually leading, and then it becomes clear whether we are honestly living in line with our beliefs or if our actions sometimes stray from our truths.

We tend to feel "lost" when we wander too far from our core values. If happiness is when what we think, what we say, and what we do, are all in harmony (as Gandhi suggested), then living out of alignment is what causes our internal conflict, hypocrisy, and dis-ease. That's when we try to numb our pain or run away from our troubles, but the solution isn't outside of us, it's within.

I'm not going to give you a list of core values to follow; you will inevitably realize your own truths by answering each day's questions, every month. That's how you'll get closer to deciding who you want to be in relation to the world around you. After all, your beliefs don't make you a better person, your behavior does. And since our actions convey our priorities, let's bridge the gap between our words and how we act in the world!

Each month has its own theme, a random but delicious recipe, some inspirational quotes, and as always, the intention to awaken, enlighten, enrich, and inspire.

With much love from your brother,
Timber Hawkeye

Cilantro Lime Rice

This month's recipe is a new twist on an old staple: Rice (also works with quinoa).

Cook your white or brown rice as you normally would (except use vegetable broth instead of water for added flavor and nutritional value).

If you're using an Instant-Pot, combine 1 cup of white rice with 1.5 cups of broth (or 1 cup of brown rice with only 1 cup of broth), a splash of olive oil, and a pinch of salt. Cook white rice on high pressure for 3 minutes (then wait about ten minutes for the pressure to release), or brown rice on high pressure for 23 minutes (plus a few minutes for the pressure to naturally release).

In a blender, combine the juice of a lime or two, a bunch of cilantro, and a little olive oil, and blend to a beautiful, pesto-like paste. Mix it with the COOKED rice, serve, and enjoy. It's so delicious, you'll forget it's a side dish!

January 1

The theme for this month is **Letting Go**.

This time of year, there is plenty of buzz about setting new goals, starting new habits, and buying new stuff, but very little attention is placed on what we must leave behind in order to accommodate all that change. For example, to combat their high levels of stress, many people turn to yoga, meditation, and exercise, which can be great, but if they do it without addressing the existing causes of stress, something as beneficial as yoga just adds to their already overflowing plates. So before we talk about what you can add to your life, what can you leave behind as you start the new year?

_____

_____

What do you feel when you imagine life without it?

_____

Have you tried letting go of it before?   _____

If so, what will be different this time around?

_____

January 2

Along with "New Year Resolutions," there is a surge in new gym memberships, a spike in healthy recipe sharing, and a sudden drop in cigarette purchases. By March, however, many people return to their old habits of not exercising enough, eating junk food, and actually smoking more than before. To make sure you don't fall off the wagon, go ahead and pick a goal to which this journal will hold you accountable every month.

_____

_____

What promise or resolve have you made to yourself in the past and actually stuck to?

_____

_____

_____

_____

_____

_____

January 3

My friends Lauren and Dwayne are the same age, yet Lauren is young and full of life (vibrant, joyous, social, and stays physically active by swimming, hiking, surfing three times a week, going on road trips, etc.), while Dwayne is full of excuses and resentment of his "old age" (even though they were born the same year). So my question to you is this: what age do you feel, and how is that affected by the life you choose to lead?

_____

_____

Who, your own age, inspires you to be more like them?

_____

Who, your own age, inspires you to be less like them?

_____

Think of times you've complained about your age. List three things about your age for which you are grateful:

_____

_____

"Everything I've ever let go of had claw marks in it."

I often encourage people to eliminate extra "stuff" from around their house (unused dishes, moldy towels, torn bed sheets, empty bottles of shampoo, etc.), not because there is anything inherently "wrong" with having that stuff, but because there is tremendous benefit from exercising the muscle of releasing our grip and letting go. The way we do one thing is the way we do all things, so when we get into the habit of loosening our white-knuckle attachment to clothes that no longer fit us, used candles with buried wicks, or seasoning packets in our pantry that have lost all their flavor a decade ago, we also make it easier to let go of old attitudes, judgments, resentments, stereotypes, grudges, and beliefs. Of the many opinions you hoard in your head, what closely-held belief are you beginning to doubt?

_____

What new perspective can replace that old judgment?

_____

What lessons did you get from keeping that judgment for as long and you did and from letting it go?

_____

January 5

I used to hate rules because they felt restricting. I now think of rules as buffers (like bumpers at bowling alleys to keep the ball from falling into the gutter). Rules set healthy boundaries. How do you feel about rules?

_____

_____

Can you think of rules you appreciate?

_____

As a personal rule, my neighbor doesn't eat after 8pm, and my old roommate was strict about not going to bed with dishes in the sink. What are your personal rules?

_____

_____

Do you ever break any of them? _____

Is it maybe time to change some of them?

_____

Now, how do you feel about rules?

_____

January 6

What does success mean to you? _____

_____

Do you feel successful? _____

I used to measure success by the amount of money someone had in the bank, their highest level of education, the car they drove, or the job they had, but now that I believe we are here to learn to be selfless and giving, forgiving and kind, as long as people (myself included) are heading in that general direction and do more good than harm, helping others with the intention to awaken, enlighten, enrich, and inspire, then they (and I), regardless of financial wealth, are deemed successful. When I think of all the experiences in my life for which I am grateful, I feel abundant success and happiness. Instead of thinking of success as a final destination, therefore, in what can you succeed today?

_____

Who do you consider successful and by what definition?

_____

Who do you consider unsuccessful, and why?

_____

One of the greatest gifts my father has given me is the freedom from obligation. He told me to never do something out of a sense of obligation (which is often pushed on us by others), but rather do everything because I full-heartedly want to do it and/or because I see the benefit of doing it (be it for myself or another). As a result, I grew up perplexed by people who say things like, "I have to go to this birthday party tonight," implying they don't want to go but feel obligated to attend. I remember thinking that if it was my own birthday party they were talking about, and if I knew that's how they felt, then I would rather them not show up. Is there something you've recently done (or are scheduled to do) that you would rather not do at all? And please don't say 'I'd rather not go to work' because you ultimately DO want to go to work as it affords you the life you choose to live; I'm asking if there are "social obligations" from which you'd rather bow out?

_____

The difference between obligation and responsibility is:

_____

How do you feel about being free from obligation?

_____

January 8

When I was a kid, I had the habit of biting my nails. My parents tried every method imaginable to get me to stop, including application of a bitter gel on my fingertips intended to stop me from putting my fingers in my mouth, but I got used to the taste and kept biting my nails just the same. Until one day, I just stopped. We are creatures of habit, so we can get in the habit of breaking them. What habit do you have that prevents you from leading the life you ultimately want to live?

_____

_____

Can you replace that habit with a healthier one?

_____

What habits are you grateful for?

_____

What habits are you glad to have broken in the past?

_____

_____

_____

"If you don't heal from what hurt you,
you will end bleeding on people who didn't cut you."

One of the biggest challenges in life is forgiving those who have wronged us. The thought that someone "owes you an apology" is crippling because it gives power to the very person you do not want controlling your life. So instead of asking you who owes you an apology, I'm asking who can you forgive?

_____

Being mad at someone for being how they've always been is rather silly when you really think about it. If anything, I get mad at myself for not coming to terms with it sooner. Can you forgive yourself?

_____

_____

Is there something from that experience for which you are grateful?

_____

How do you feel when you think of how your life would be when you no longer carry that anger or resentment?

_____

January 10

Once you know something, it is difficult if not impossible to un-know it. As a kid, my sister loved clam chowder until she learned what clams were. Then she practically gagged at the thought of ever eating them again. In that case, her ignorance was bliss. Is there something you have recently found out that you wish you hadn't?

Once we learn something new, it becomes difficult to continue doing what we were doing when we didn't know any better. If we continue doing it, then we feel like hypocrites. But if we stop doing it, we feel empowered to change other aspects of our lives that we now know are detrimental to us. What change have you recently made in your life because of new information?

Do you feel like you have grown because of this change or are you more restricted by it?

Who shared the new information with you ? Have you expressed your gratitude to them?

January 11

> Things only appear to be falling apart.
> They are actually falling into place.

Have you ever mistaken a life lesson for a soul mate? I know I have. And when that relationship ended, I felt like all was lost and like I'd never love or be loved again. A bit melodramatic in hindsight, especially since feelings aren't facts, but that's the beauty of the experience: I have learned not to take my feelings too seriously, and to not believe everything I think, either. I'm grateful that some things didn't work out the way I once wanted them to. In your own life, what has "fallen apart" that actually helped today fall into place?

_____

_____

What/who are you glad to no longer have in your life?

_____

_____

Is there something to which you're currently attached that you might actually benefit from letting go instead of insisting on hanging onto?

_____

_____

January 12

I've learned so much from my mistakes, I think I'm gonna go out there and make some more. Can you think of a "wrong turn" you don't regret taking?

_____

_____

If you believe in fate, was your fate to make the mistake or to learn the lesson?

_____

When did life try to teach you that same lesson before you had to learn it the hard way?

_____

What lessons are you being taught right now?

_____

_____

_____

_____

_____

January 13

"People sacrifice their health in order to make money.
Then they sacrifice money to recuperate their health.
And then, they are so anxious about the future,
they do not enjoy the present moment.
As a result, they don't live in the present or the future,
they live as if they are never going to die,
and then they die having never truly lived."
—The Dalai Lama,
when asked what surprises him the most.

On what do you spend too much money?

_____

What would be a better use of your money?

_____

On what do you spend too much energy?

_____

What would be a better use of your energy?

_____

Repeat after me:
"I'm grateful for the money and energy I have."

_____

January 14

If you wake up each morning thinking you didn't get enough sleep the night before, or that perhaps you're not pretty enough, rich enough, successful enough, healthy enough, or anything-else-enough, it means you begin each day with the mindset of scarcity, and experience every moment from a place of lack. A mantra is something you repeat to yourself over and over again until it becomes the soundtrack to your life. If your mantra is "more," then you'll never have enough. If your mantra is "poor me," you will find a way to identify as a victim in every situation... you get the idea. What do you think is your mantra?

_____

Can you recall a time when you had a very different outlook on life and what your core perspective or mantra was back then?

_____

What do you think would be a really great mantra to have from this point forward?

_____

"Things turn out best for those who make the best of the way things turn out." —Art Linkletter

January 15

We're halfway through the month; time for a check-in. Do you recall what you wanted to leave behind and not carry into the new year? How's that working out?

_____

_____

How can you impress yourself today?

_____

_____

What's going well and feels great right now?

_____

Gandhi said "Our actions convey our priorities." If you were to monitor your own daily behavior, what would your choices indicate you value most in life?

_____

_____

Is that the same thing you would tell someone is the most important thing to you, or is it different?

_____

January 16

Eleanor Roosevelt said, "No one can make you feel inferior without your consent," and I not only agree with her, I believe no one can make you feel ANYTHING without your consent! For example, you can say something offensive to me, and I can choose not to be offended. Alternatively, I can choose to be hurt, angry, upset, or frustrated, but that wouldn't be your fault. If I don't control my own attitude, it will control me. Tempting as it is to blame other people for everything that's wrong in your life, what role are **you** playing (or not playing) in contributing to your anguish?

_____

_____

_____

_____

What have you done in the past that you are now really glad you did?

_____

_____

Which of your life skills are you most proud of?

_____

January 17

What do you have a hard time believing?

_____

How would your life change if you believed it?

_____

_____

The opposite of what you know is also true (to somebody else, somewhere else, because of their time, place, or circumstance.) What you believe becomes your reality and often the only truth you see. Can you think of a circumstance or relationship in your life that would improve if you were to acknowledge that the different beliefs of someone else are just as valid as your own?

_____

_____

_____

_____

_____

_____

January 18

Ever since we were kids, we've been exposed to the concept of at least two opposing forces within us (originally depicted in cartoons as an angel on one shoulder and a devil on the other). I now think of them as simply the goodness within and the ego within. Selfless vs. Selfish, or Generous vs. Greedy, etc. Can you distinguish between the two in your own mind, and perhaps give each of them a name?

_____

Taking the monastic vows is essentially a commitment to only follow the goodness within regardless of the life we had led beforehand. I'm not suggesting everyone become monks and nuns, but we can all commit to at least bring awareness to the two forces within us, and work on what we ultimately know is best (not just for ourselves, but for the ripple affect we have on everything and everyone around us). From that point of view, what decision are you making in your life right now that isn't in line with what you know is best?

_____

_____

Can you think of an alternative route that's more in line with the selfless, kinder, gentler, wiser, part of you?

_____

January 19

Words have power, and some words trigger a strong, negative reaction in us. I wonder, however, if words are just words and we give them that power (which is clearly evident by the fact that some people are deeply affected by a word that doesn't phase others in any way). The word God, for example, used to bother me because I associated it with the definition of a God I was given as a child. It took some redefining for me to make peace with it and now I use it all the time. The word "Corporate," as another example, thrilled me at one point in my life and disgusted me in another. I now realize that my strong aversion to certain words was detrimental to my own inner peace (like a minefield where a single step in the wrong direction can cause me to shut down). Can you think of any words to which you've given too much power that you can now get back by maybe using it as a practice to diffuse it?

_____

_____

_____

_____

Where did you get the initial definition of that word?

_____

January 20

A friend of mine has a 16 year old son who recently got out of Juvenile Detention for dealing drugs since he was 13. He is now determined to stay clean, and she's committed to helping him stay there, but you wouldn't believe how many people judge her for buying him cigarettes. She's happy they're just cigarettes! Never criticize what you haven't even made the effort to understand, because once you understand, there is nothing left to criticize. What presumptions, prejudices, and stereotypes do you have about certain people?

_____

_____

Can you imagine how that would change if your child fell in love with someone who fits that stereotype?

_____

Can you imagine how your views would change if one of those people saved your life?

_____

How would your life change if you let that opinion go?

_____

_____

January 21

"What you are afraid to do is a clear indication of the next thing you need to do." —Ralph Waldo Emerson

Was I scared to move to Hawaii without a job lined up or a place to live? Of course I was! But I did it anyway. Acknowledge the fear, but don't be so scared of it. You've made it through everything that has happened in your life so far, which means your track record's 100%. Trust that you'll make it through whatever comes next. That's not even blind faith, it's the same trust with which a bird sits on a branch unafraid of the branch breaking: her trust is in her own wings, not in the branch. What would you do if you weren't afraid?

_____

_____

What's scarier for you: taking a leap of faith or staying in your current situation for a few more years?

_____

Can you think of a time you've done something that was initially scary and later turned out to be less of a big deal than it seemed in your head?

_____

January 22

We often take our health for granted until the moment we no longer have it. What physical abilities are you most grateful for right now?

_____

_____

We tend to take our homes for granted, our beds, indoor plumbing, electricity, and Internet access (among other modern conveniences). What privilege are you most grateful for right now that you haven't acknowledged in quite some time or perhaps ever?

_____

_____

_____

_____

_____

_____

_____

January 23

"Nature doesn't hurry, yet everything is accomplished."
—Lao Tzu

We have much to learn from nature: trees show us how to let things go when they release their leaves every fall, rivers teach us to go with the flow, and the unpredictability of weather keeps us from thinking anything is under our control. Just as we go to school to learn certain lessons, we must spend time with nature to better understand our part in it. It's been said that enlightenment is when a wave realizes it is the ocean, which is a brilliant depiction of our interconnectedness. How can you connect with nature this week?

_____

Can you think of a time you went against nature and it backfired (trying to speed things up or slow things down, perhaps? Trying to turn what is inherently temporary into something permanent, maybe?)

_____

_____

When you close your eyes and travel in your mind to the most ideal locale, are you by the ocean? The mountains? Among trees? By a lake? What's the weather like?

_____

January 24

Conversations can enlighten us if we actively listen, or they can further inflate our ever-hungry egos if all we do is talk. Can you think of a time you chose to bite your tongue and you're glad you did?

_____

_____

A time you would have been better off keeping quiet:

_____

If someone tells me the sky is green and I believe it to be blue, I don't argue with them or try to prove them wrong, I just walk away from that conversation with the newfound knowledge that to some people the sky looks green. The blueness of my sky is not threatened by how green someone else perceives it to be. Can you stay in your truth while simultaneously making peace with the fact that the opposite is true to someone else?

_____

_____

When you feel the need to correct someone without being asked, what's that about? Can you let it go?

_____

We're nearing the end of the month, and after all the food-for-thought you've been chewing since the first of the year, what changes will you make in your life?

_____

_____

In my twenties, when I decided to be an athlete, it wasn't about winning any tournaments, it was about playing volleyball every day. If we focus too much on a destination, then we miss out on the journey. My fondest memories aren't of any medals won, they're of the athletic lifestyle I had back then. In that sense of the word "goal," what would you like to accomplish this year? (That is to say, on what journey would you like to embark, not a destination you wish to reach)

_____

_____

_____

_____

What goal have you set for yourself in the past that you are now living?

_____

January 26

If our happiness depends on something we can lose, we will spend our entire life afraid of losing it. Other people can make me smile, but they can't make me happy; that's my job (it's my sole/soul responsibility). To that end, my happiness does not depend on something I can lose (like money, my youth, or physical ability), nor does it depend on someone I can lose (parent, spouse, friend, pet), it depends on who I am. Not only will I always be me because I can't be anyone else, I will always be fine-tuning, growing, and evolving "me." With that mindset, what contributes to you being happy?

_____

_____

_____

Having said all that, it IS important to acknowledge what makes us smile as well. Who and what in your life makes you smile the most?

_____

_____

How does it feel to not depend on someone else for your happiness?

_____

"If we do not openly repent our wrongdoings, we are more likely to repeat them." —Cheng Yen

That which weighs heavily on our conscience traps us in a game of hide-and-seek with our true selves year after year. One of the most liberating exercises to break that cycle is repentance (to feel or express sincere regret or remorse about one's wrongdoing). So, in the spirit of making peace with all that has been so we can leave it behind, what would you like to confess?

_____

_____

_____

This isn't about "coming clean" with someone else so that you "feel better" (especially if doing so would be detrimental to *their* life), it's about forgiving yourself. Do not identify today with anything from the past. How will you behave going forward? What would forgiving yourself look like?

_____

_____

_____

January 28

The reward you get for being patient in one part of your life is more patience in others. When I encourage people to do jigsaw or sudoku puzzles, for example, they often say, "I don't have patience for that." But that's EXACTLY why I suggest it! It's by practicing patience that we become more patient. It's like when people say "I can't do yoga, I'm not flexible." That's what yoga is for (among many other benefits). So, in what areas of your life can you use more patience?

_____

_____

In what ways can you intentionally exercise patience as if it was a muscle so that it's strong when you need it most (parking farthest from entrances, solving puzzles, chewing your food, driving in the slow lane, etc.)

_____

_____

What required extra patience from you recently, and what did you do to remain calm?

_____

_____

We are responsible for our own happiness. What can you start doing today that you know would be beneficial to your overall well-being?

_____

_____

What unhealthy food item can you start substituting with a healthier one?

_____

What unhealthy drink item can you start substituting with a healthier one?

_____

How much time would you like to spend outdoors each day, doing what?

_____

I have an "Under 10 floors I will use the stairs" rule for myself. If you're physically able, how many floors will you commit to climbing by stairs before you consider taking the elevator?

_____

January 30

Take a moment to think about how grateful you are for all the gifts in your life. On a scale from 1 to 10, how grateful would you say you are? _____

From 1 to 10, how happy are you? _____

There is a connection between the level of joy you experience in life when you are grateful, and the level of frustration you experience when you're ungrateful. **What** are you grateful for? (**Not who** are you grateful for). Don't list the names of people or their relation to you, list elements in your life for which you are grateful.

_____

_____

_____

_____

Now go ahead and list people in your life for whom you are grateful and why.

_____

_____

_____

January 31

We are a work in progress heading toward more progress, not perfection. What could you have done better this month?

_____

I remember outright lying to people when I was young in a desperate attempt to impress them. It backfired, of course, because I knew I was lying, which was depressive to me regardless of how impressive it may have sounded to them. I've since been taught to pause before I speak and ask myself if what I'm about to say is true, necessary, and kind. If it's not all three, then I don't need to say it out loud. It has kept me quiet on many occasions. Of the three: Is it true, is it necessary, and is it kind, which is most difficult for you?

_____

_____

What do you think fuels your impulse to say out loud what doesn't meet the criteria?

_____

_____

_____

CPSIA information can be obtained
at www.ICGtesting.com
Printed in the USA
BVHW051553220119
538283BV00027B/1903/P